The Ot1

by Gordon Wood

Dept of Biology, Universit

Contents

The Otter
By Gordon Woodroffe

Published by The Mammal Society

The Mammal Society
Registered Charity No. 278918
Registered Office:
The Mammal Society
2B Inworth Street
London
SW11 3EP

3rd Edition
ISBN 978-0-906282-63-2

This is one of a series of booklets on British mammals published by
The Mammal Society

The Mammal Society is most grateful to the Environment Agency for their
generous sponsorship of this booklet

Environment
Agency
Asiantaeth yr
Amgylchedd

Photographs by Laurie Campbell (cover, pages 7, 18),
Niall Benvie (page 4 above), Andrew Moorhouse (pages 4 below, 15),
Hans Kruuk (page 11),
Gordon Woodroffe (pages 5, 6, 7, 9, 10, 12).

Layout and printing by SP Press, Units 1 & 2, Mendip Vale Trading Estate,
Cheddar Business Park, Cheddar, Somerset BS27 3EL

Recognition and relatives

Otters are members of the family Mustelidae, which is the largest family of the order Carnivora, containing 67 species. The Mustelidae contains five subfamilies, including the Mustelinae (weasels, martens, polecats), Melinae (badgers), Mellivorinae (honey badger) and Mephitinae (skunks). The fifth subfamily – the Lutrinae – contains at least thirteen species of otters. The one species of European otter *(Lutra lutra)* is the subject of this booklet. This species ranges from the British Isles to the rain forests of southeastern Asia and from North Africa to northern Russia and Finland; it is also known as the Eurasian otter. Sadly, it is now scarce in or absent from many parts of its former range. The British population is now one of the largest in Europe, with many individuals living around the coasts of Scotland. Although these do swim and feed in the sea, they are not sea otters. The sea otter *(Enhydra lutris)* is a quite different species found along the Pacific coast of Alaska and California. It is the most aquatic of carnivorous mammals, even more so than the seals, eating, sleeping, mating, giving birth and rearing its young at sea.

The Eurasian otter is one of Britain's largest Carnivores. Males can weigh up to 11kg and are 30% heavier than females. The thick, long, tapering tail is one of its characteristic features. The otter has a flat head and broad muzzle surrounded by long stiff vibrissae (whiskers). The fur is a medium to dark brown colour except for a pale throat and light underparts. Some have white throat patches, which vary in extent and can be useful in identification of individuals. When wet, the coat looks darker and, as the otter leaves the water, the hairs are flattened giving a 'sleek' appearance. Otters have short legs and a long body, which leans slightly forward when the animal is walking, giving it a humpy outline.

The only other semi-aquatic mammal in the British Isles, which is likely to be mistaken for an otter, is the introduced American mink *(Mustela vison)*, a newcomer to our fauna which has been expanding its range since the late 1950s. Although similar in shape to mink, otters are twice as long and, on average, nearly ten times heavier. This is one of the most useful distinguishing features in the field; mink are smaller than a domestic cat, otters are much larger. In addition mink usually have much darker, almost black, fur against which the white chin spots appear particularly conspicuous. They also have a fluffy, cylindrical tail.

Aquatic adaptations

The otter's elongated, sinuous body, webbed feet and muscular tail make it well adapted for an aquatic lifestyle. The foot webbing extends for much of the length of each toe and is much more extensive than in non-aquatic carnivores e.g. domestic dog *(Canis familiaris)*. Compared with other mammals of the same size, the paws are also quite large, probably to give more thrust when otters are swimming. The tail is broad at the base, tapering towards the tip where it is noticeably flattened from top to bottom. When swimming slowly, otters use all four legs in a dog-paddle fashion, but accelerate by tucking their forelimbs into their sides and moving their hindlegs in powerful strokes.

The structural design of otter fur provides the thermal insulation essential for the otter's aquatic lifestyle. The thick fur has two types of hair, an outer layer of long coarse guard hairs (each 20-40mm long) and a dense under-layer (10mm thick) which is so dense that it looks almost like the skin itself. This under-layer traps an insulating layer of air, which helps to keep the body warm and dry during long swimming or diving bouts. Otters usually stay under water for quite a short period; typical dives last between 10–40 seconds and few exceed 45 seconds. In shallow water they usually make much shorter dives than at greater depths.

A swimming otter

In clear bright water seeing prey poses few problems. Human eyes are not adapted to focus sharply under water unless there is a layer of air between the water and the surface of the eye, which is why divers wear face masks. Otters, however, can adjust the curvature of the eye lens to such an extent that, in bright light, they see as clearly under water as above it. At night and in murky waters, however, they have to rely on their long, sensitive whiskers to detect prey.

Coastal and freshwater otters

In the early 1980s not enough was known about otters for them to be studied with any degree of confidence in the places where they were scarce. Shetland, however, provided an ideal locality for carrying out basic

A coastal otter sprainting in water

ecological and behavioural studies. Here otters are common, live along accessible coasts and are active during the day. These otters and those occupying other marine habitats on the west coast of Scotland are described as coastal otters. They are the same species as those inhabiting inland, freshwater river systems but a distinction needs to be made because research has shown some behavioural differences between them.

Field signs

With the exception of parts of the west coast of Scotland and around the Orkney and Shetland Islands there are few places where it is possible to watch otters in the wild for any length of time. In many parts of their range the problem of finding otters is compounded by their nocturnal and secretive nature and the fact that they can occupy very large ranges covering many kilometres of waterways. Fortunately, their presence in an area can be detected by the distinctive field signs they leave. Indeed, all the national surveys of otter distribution in the British Isles have relied heavily on the interpretation of field signs.

Spraints

Otter faeces, known as spraints, are the most common field signs. Otters have a very powerful digestive system and only bones, fish scales, fur, feathers and insect remains pass right through the gut. In fresh spraints the undigested items are coated with mucus. Fresh spraints are often black and have a pleasant, sweet-musky odour, which can persist for several weeks. This has been aptly described by Rob Strachan as smelling like jasmine tea. The size and shape can vary from a tiny blob or tarry smear to a compact cylindrical dropping of up to about 6cm long, with males producing the smallest spraints and cubs the largest. As spraints dry out their colour fades and they crumble to give a grey ashy deposit. The musk-like scent is the best diagnostic character to use in distinguishing spraints from other droppings, especially those of mink, which have a most unpleasant smell when fresh and are also more uniform and taper at the ends.

A rock marked by spraint

Otters deposit spraints and sometimes jelly-like secretions at prominent places throughout their range. These can be found along rivers and streams on large rocks and boulders, fallen tree trunks, logs, grass tufts on top of river banks and tree roots, in hollows under tree roots and on concrete ledges under bridges. Spraints may also be left at the entrances to holts (dens) and other resting places. Well-used otter paths usually have spraint piles at intervals along them, notably where the animal leaves and enters the water. Sometimes if there is no obvious landmark an otter will make one by scraping up a small heap of sand, soil or a grass twist (known as sign heaps) and spraint on top.

Coastal otters leave trails at intervals along the shore which they mark regularly with piles of spraints. They also mark resources such as freshwater pools and holts in this way. Spraint sites are also used for urination and this regular supply of fertilizer turns the surrounding grass bright green or causes algae to grow on stones around spraints. The high levels of nitrogen may eventually kill the vegetation.

Well used sprainting site at a freshwater pool on Mull.

Footprints

The five-toed otter footprint, arching around the front of a large pad, is another useful field sign. Good, clear footprints are most likely to be found in soft mud, snow or on sand flats. The prints are easy to recognise when all five toes show up. If the ground is soft, claw marks and webbing may also be visible. The width of the footprints ranges from 5 to 7cm; footprints greater than 6.5cm probably indicate males, while those less than 4.5cm wide may be evidence of a cub. It is not possible to distinguish female tracks from those of juvenile males. Great care needs to be taken in the interpretation of track size as this can vary widely with the softness of the ground and how the animal is travelling. All too often only four or even three toes are visible because the small outer ones do not register. They can then be easily confused with other mammal tracks. In such cases the most useful feature to distinguish otter tracks from dog or fox tracks is that otter footprints are not symmetrical; the left half is not a mirror image of the right. Mink and badgers *(Meles meles)*, like all the mustelids, have five toes. However, mink toe prints are much more pointed, and are considerably smaller with a width of 3-3.5 cm. Badger footprints, on the other hand, have a characteristic bean-shaped pad with the five toes appearing in a nearly straight line. In other words, no toe print is set further back from the others. Badgers also have much longer claws.

Feeding remains

Otter tracks along a sandy beach

Slides

Remains of fish and frogs are often left by otters. However, these can be difficult to distinguish from those left by competing predators unless footprints and/or spraints are found nearby.

Otters may create slides down river banks. They are probably no more than a quick route into the water without the need to expend too much energy.

Without doubt the best way of learning how to identify and interpret otter signs is to spend some time working alongside an experienced fieldworker.

Communication

Otters deposit spraints at prominent places throughout their range. These are impregnated with scent from the anal sacs which lie on each side of the rectum and open into the anus through short ducts. In areas heavily marked by coastal otters the scent is strong enough to be detected from several metres away by human observers. Consequently otters have little difficulty in perceiving scent messages. Otters can also discriminate between the spraints from different animals, all of which suggest that 'sprainting' is an important means of communication. However, precisely what is being communicated is open to interpretation.

Cubs with their mother, who is sprainting on seaweed.

Obviously all otters have to defaecate. The term 'sprainting' refers to the deposition of droppings in conspicuous places. After emerging from the water an otter will often inspect a spraint site, sniff it, then spraint and/or urinate, curling its tail slightly upwards. Studies on coastal otters have also shown that sprainting patterns vary between individuals. Some otters spraint often and obviously, while others spraint little and unobtrusively, and sometimes in the water. Other research indicates that males may have a higher sprainting frequency than females. Their spraints tend to be appreciably smaller than those of females, often little more than tiny droplets. Sprainting appears to be much higher in winter than in summer almost everywhere. Jim Conroy and Hans Kruuk found that the seasonal differences in the number of spraints along the shores of Shetland were not caused by the coastal animals spending more or less time there during winter and summer, but by individual otters actually sprainting more often on land in the winter. The Sprainting frequency recorded in March was 12 times higher than in June, not because otters produced fewer scats in summer, but because at this time of the year they more readily defaecate while swimming.

In Shetland high sprainting rates coincided with low prey availability and also when cubs were nearly full grown but still with their mothers. There was no overall significant difference in sprainting rates between otters of different sex or status, and nor were concentrations of spraints found near group territorial boundaries (see *Movements and activity*). Sprainting was associated with the start of feeding bouts and the utilisation of other resources such as fresh water and dens. More than 30% of spraints were deposited below the high tide level and were, therefore, only functional as markers for a short time. From these observations Hans Kruuk has argued that the temporal pattern of use and subsequent replenishment of resources makes it worthwhile for otters to signal to other group members that they are exploiting a resource. In doing so otters avoid aggressive encounters. In other words if sprainting is a means of communication, or even if it has a sexual function, then it is feasible that otters will only spraint at conspicuous places when population densities rise sufficiently for communication to become important. This hypothesis is supported to some degree by a study in North Yorkshire; when otter numbers were very low, sprainting was negligible but after a restocking programme sprainting intensity was high and spraints became relatively easy to find.

Vocalisations

Compared with the sociable otters, particularly the Asian short-clawed *(Aonyx cinerea)* and the Indian smooth-coated *(Lutra perspicillata)*, the more solitary Eurasian species has a limited number of vocalisations. The most famous is the 'whistle', a contact call between mother and cubs, which is little more than a high-pitched squeak. However, hearing a whistle on the river bank at night does not necessarily mean it was made by an otter; it could easily be confused with the cacophony of calls made by other riverside mammals and birds such as pipits. Cubs are particularly vocal and chitter if they are separated from other members of the family. Otters sometimes produce a quieter huff when they are investigating something unfamiliar and they also use it to warn of danger or when anxious. A number of calls, such as whickering and twittering, have also been described when the animals are in close contact. They are noisiest, however, when mating and their sounds have been variously described as "chirruping", "purring", "staccato grunts" and "squeaks". What all these convey is anyone's guess!

Habitat

Otters exploit a wide range of aquatic habitats from small ditches, moorland streams, lakes and ponds to large rivers, estuaries and coasts. The use of a particular habitat depends, however, on its suitability in providing the basic requirements of food and shelter.

Studies of rivers and inland waters in northern Scotland, for example, have shown that there is a close correlation between utilisation of streams by otters and the biomass and production of fish in them, with smaller streams preferred because their fish productivity is higher. The sexes appear to occupy somewhat different habitats, with males spending more time on large rivers and females favouring small burns and lochs. In England moorland streams are less productive and these may function more as routes connecting areas of more favourable habitats.

Holts, dens and couches

The difficulty in recognising otter resting places, refuges and holts (dens in tunnel systems and natural cavities) was highlighted in a radio-tracking study in Perthshire. Only six out of 21 holts and three out of 24 couches (resting places above ground) were clearly identifiable. Over half of the resting places were situated above ground and included piles of sticks, brambles, river debris, scrub-covered islets and depressions in bankside vegetation. Holts were often under waterside trees with well-developed root systems; those in the interlaced roots of adjacent trees with underwater entrances were particularly difficult to identify. Other radio-tracking work on the tributaries of the Rivers Dee and Don in northeast Scotland has shown the importance of reed beds for resting, breeding and feeding even when they are several kilometres away from open water. On loch shores, for example, otters hardly ever rested or slept underground, preferring reeds or thick vegetation even during the severest weather. Otters constructed their couches by biting or pulling up vegetation, which they often dragged some distance. Hans Kruuk found that on the Dinnet lochs in northeast Scotland breeding females made special covered couches from large beds of reeds. Such couches were sometimes found on a dry spot in a large reed bed, with one or two entrances at the sides and a lining of soft grass. One of the radio-tracked otters gave birth to cubs in one of these couches which was about two kilometres from the open water inhabited by other otters.

Holts were found to be far less important in freshwater habitats than in coastal areas. In Shetland otters usually constructed their own holts by digging extensive systems of tunnels and chambers which they furnished with bedding, although they sometimes used caves and rabbit warrens.

In Shetland a strong correlation was found between numbers of otters and holts. These were mainly located on peaty, undrained coasts with easy access to fresh water, which the animals need for washing the salt out of their fur. This process is essential for animals living in a marine environment, because without it their fur loses its insulating properties and this can lead to pneumonia. Compared with otter numbers in non-agricultural or peaty coasts, those in areas of Shetland drained for agriculture were very low. Possibly the absence of fresh water makes these habitats less suitable. With such a variation in habitats throughout the UK it is very difficult to define precisely what constitutes an optimum otter environment.

Good otter habitat,
North Yorkshire

Movements and activity

Although otters may travel large distances, most adults stay in a well-defined area (home range), within which they feed, rest and reproduce. A territory, on the other hand, is an area containing vital resources which is defended from other members of the same species. Territories are not defended for their own sake, but for the resources contained within them. Unfortunately the areas used by otters, especially coastal animals, do not always fit into such neat categories and frequently overlap in a complicated pattern. To avoid confusion I do not differentiate between home ranges and territories but refer to the areas used as 'ranges'. Like those of water voles *(Arvicola terrestris)*, otter ranges are measured as lengths of river bank or coast rather than the usual areas of most other mammals.

Studies in Shetland have shown that groups of reproducing females occupy ranges which exclude other females. Groups had range sizes of 4.7, 6.4 and 14 km; the number of females within the groups varied from two to five individuals. The size of the ranges is largely influenced by the spacing of different types of coastline required for the otters to capitalise on the seasonal availability of important prey species. Male ranges overlapped with those of several female groups and were larger. Male ranges also overlapped extensively among themselves. Habitats used by the two sexes varied, with males spending more time on exposed coasts. Within the female group range, every animal used the whole length of the coast occupied by their group, but in addition appeared to have an individual core range in which they spent most of their time. There was little or no overlap between the core ranges of different animals.

In Scottish rivers females are solitary but in freshwater lakes they share territories. Linear ranges in fresh water are very much larger than in Shetland and other coastal sites; 25-40 km for females and up to 70 km for males. However, these comparisons need to be treated cautiously because in Scotland many of the freshwater streams used by otters are no more than one metre wide. On the other hand, coastal animals fish in a strip up to 100m wide, the degree of utilisation generally decreasing with depth.

Thus, while it is convenient to calculate otter ranges as coastal length, in terms of total area they may be much more similar to freshwater ranges.

In freshwater systems studied in Sweden, otter social structure conformed to the more usual mustelid pattern with each female or family having its own range. These were rarely contiguous and those of a single male often overlapped with more than one female range. On one occasion a male otter was killed and within days his range was occupied by a neighbouring male. In a Perthshire radiotracking study the male's range overlapped those of two females. While the females spent the majority of their time in the most productive and secure parts of their ranges, the male was distinctly more adventurous and regularly patrolled the full extent of his range.

An otter grooming itself after swimming

Coastal otters in Shetland appear to catch most of their prey during the day, being most active in the morning and early evening in summer and with a single activity peak after mid-day in winter. These are the best times for fishing because the key prey species are inactive, hiding under stones and weeds. Conversely in fresh water, otters are largely nocturnal, emerging around sunset and maintaining activity throughout the night when some of the important prey species, particularly salmonids, are torpid and easier to catch. Thus the different activity patterns between coastal and freshwater otters seem to be partly regulated by how easy it is to obtain prey.

Although otters are highly aquatic mammals, a detailed study on coastal animals showed that they spent about 70% of a 24-hour period inside the holt. During their active phase hunting occupied about 45% of their time, eating 5%, grooming 20% and sleeping outside the holt approximately 25%. Unspecified activities accounted for the remaining 5%. Grooming is particularly important; the otter's very dense and thick fur is essential for thermal insulation because otters have virtually no subcutaneous body fat.

Thus washing the salt out of their fur in freshwater pools, rolling and rubbing themselves in seaweed and/or grass (rolling places) helps the fur to recover and regain its insulating properties after swimming and diving bouts in the sea.

Energetics

Swimming is energetically tremendously expensive. The colder the water the more energy otters use. An otter may spend four to six hours per day foraging in the water. If fish become more difficult to catch, for example when they are scarcer (see *Mortality and survival*), an otter must spend longer in the water to find sufficient food. This means that it will need considerably more than its average daily intake of about one kilogramme of food to make up for energy lost during the extra time spent hunting. Therefore, it has to forage even longer, getting even colder and this can lead to high mortalities.

Diet

The Eurasian otter feeds primarily on fish, which make up 70–95% of its diet. Other animals, including crayfish and amphibians, can also be important prey items depending on season and their local abundance. As otters are nocturnal throughout most of Britain, knowledge of their diet has been derived by analysing the indigestible remains in spraints, which reliably reflect the prey species ingested. Vertebrae and scales are the most commonly found fish remains and these can be identified, together with fur and feathers, either by comparing them with a reference collection of bones from fish caught in the locality or by using an appropriate key. The *Guide to the identification of prey remains in otter spraint,* published by The Mammal Society, includes both freshwater and marine prey species, and is recommended. There are many anecdotes regarding the otter's preferred prey. In reality numerous dietary studies have shown that otters are not indiscriminate in the fish and amphibians they take. Otters rarely pursue fast-swimming fish but concentrate on slow, bottom-living or resting fish, especially those with high lipid contents like eels and salmonids. The fact that such species are inactive at night probably explains why otters in England tend to be nocturnal.

Seasonal variations in diet

In Deeside eels predominate in the diet around mid-winter and after mid-summer, with perch occurring in the highest frequency in February and March. Bird remains are found more frequently in winter and also in mid-summer, together with a higher proportion of mammals. Although eels are taken in quantity throughout the year on the Somerset Levels, there is a significant drop in fish prey and an increase in the number of birds taken during summer. In northeast Scotland the consumption of amphibians increases in late winter and spring when frogs and common toads are either hibernating or spawning. Frogs and toads are also seasonally important in rivers in the North York Moors National Park. The proportion of salmonids taken on these waterways, however, appears to be constant throughout the year. In the river Esk, where salmonids and eels dominate the diet, bullheads occur in significantly greater proportions during the summer.

13

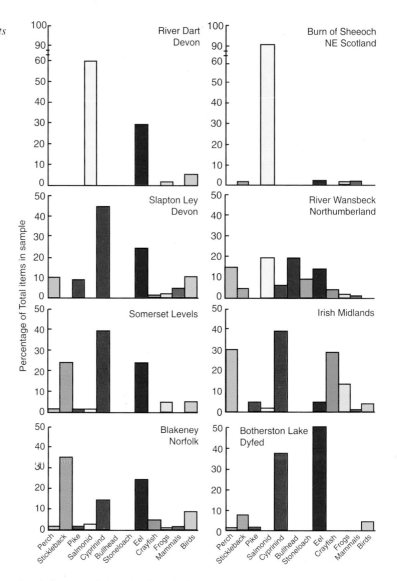

Freshwater otter diets in the British Isles. Sources: Mason & Macdonald (1986), Carrs, Kruuk & Conroy (1990) and Thom (1990). Data have been recalculated as necessary so that comparisons can be made between regions.

Predation on adult Atlantic salmon varies seasonally in the River Dee, with male fish being caught more often than females. In Shetland the biomass of the principal prey species (eelpout, rocklings and butterfish) is ten times higher in summer. During spring otters eat more 'low quality', light-weight food, such as crabs and sticklebacks.

A study along the coast of Mull showed that crustaceans made up a high proportion of the diet of otter cubs and subadults; their fish intake was much lower than that of adults. It is thought that, although fish are the preferred prey, crustaceans are much easier for young otters to catch. The low foraging efficiency of immatures may well be the reason for the

A coastal otter feeds on a crab

Otter diets in summer and winter in Shetland. Source: Kruuk, Conroy & Moorhouse 1987.

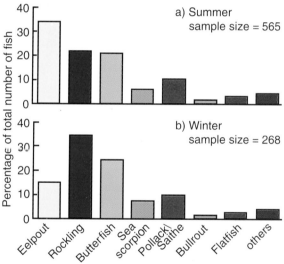

a) Summer
sample size = 565

b) Winter
sample size = 268

Percentage of total number of fish

Eelpout, Rockling, Butterfish, Sea scorpion, Pollack, Saithe, Bullrout, Flatfish, others

Eurasian otter's extended parental care compared with other mustelids. However, such exploitation of invertebrates is nothing like as great as that seen in the African clawless otters *(Aonyx* spp.*)* and sea otters which have broader teeth, well adapted to crushing hard-shelled prey. The Eurasian otter, in contrast, has narrower teeth designed for slicing flesh.

Water birds such as coots, moorhens and ducks, and their young, are likely to be most vulnerable to otters because they nest along the river bank; swallows and starlings have also been identified in otter spraints. Whether or not otters catch healthy birds or merely pick up dead and dying ones, as they explore this habitat, is unknown.

Although much rarer now, the most vulnerable mammal was the water vole which in the past often lived at high densities along river banks. Mice *(Apodemus* spp.*)*, rats *(Rattus norvegicus)*, voles *(Microtus, Clethrionomys)* and weasels *(Mustela nivalis)* have all been recorded as prey but it is unlikely that otters search actively for such relatively small species. Rabbits *(Oryctolagus cuniculus)*, on the other hand, can be a substantial item and otters have been seen catching them in their burrows in Shetland.

Predators and competition

Otters are top of the food chain and, except for humans and their dogs, have no natural predators (except for wolves *(Canis lupus)* elsewhere in their wide geographical range). Several other species, e.g. kingfishers, herons and mergansers, prey on similar fish species to otters but unless present in large numbers they are unlikely to represent serious competition.

Introduced mink were once thought to be the otter's main competitor but this has been shown not to be the case; mink tend to eat a much higher proportion of terrestrial prey. While fish make up 20-60% of their total diet, mink are far less well adapted to catch them than otters.

Concern has also been expressed that mink could be a physical threat to otters. The converse is, however, more likely with evidence from Russia of mink remains being found in otter spraints. In that same area, fur trappers complained that otters were driving mink away!

Breeding

In England there are records of otter cubs being born at all times of the year. In Shetland, however, 85% are born during the summer months (May to August) with over half between May and June. A seasonal trend is also apparent in northwest Scotland. In the Netherlands more cubs are recorded during the summer months while in Germany otters breed in both spring and summer. For Swedish and Russian otters, spring is favoured for breeding, yet coastal populations in Norway are non-seasonal in this respect.

Coastal otters in Shetland breed in the summer to take advantage of the strong fluctuation of fish density with time of year. The biomass of fish on which otters principally feed (eelpout, rocklings and butterfish) is about ten times greater during the summer than during winter and early spring. This means that food availability is at its peak when females are lactating, the time of maximum energy requirements in mammalian reproduction. The variable breeding patterns in other areas are open to interpretation. In England food is generally available throughout the year but in Sweden, where lakes are frozen for most of the winter and otters mainly fish in streams, the cubs are probably born early in the year to ensure that they are independent by the time of severest weather.

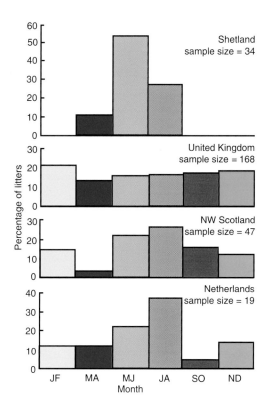

Monthly variation in the births of otter litters in Britain and the Netherlands

Eurasian otters breed when they are about two years old. Although capable of having young every year, only about 60% do so. The reasons for this are unclear but may be linked to the quality of habitat and overall otter density.

Otters have a gestation period of nine weeks. Cubs are born blind and helpless but fully furred. In freshwater populations litter sizes can vary from one to five cubs, but two or three are the norm. Coastal otters, on the other hand, appear to have smaller litters; in Shetland the average is 1.8.

The development of the cubs is slow. Their eyes open at four to five weeks, with weaning beginning at seven weeks. Weaning is complete when cubs are three months old but the mother still has to catch their food. They are dependent on their mothers for several months. The family group may split up at any time between 7–12 months.

It is interesting that species as different in size as the Asian short-clawed and giant otters *(Pteronura brasiliensis)* have similar gestation periods to the Eurasian otter's, but that the similar-sized American river otter's *(Lontra canadensis)* gestation period is prolonged to 11 months because of delayed implantation. This is a system that separates the processes of fertilisation and embryo development so that each can occur at optimum times of the year. For the American river otter, mating takes place in late

An otter bitch with cubs

spring, while the embryo is implanted into the wall of the uterus in November. The cubs are born in early spring when food is most abundant.

A similar process occurs in other mustelids including sea otters, American mink, badgers and stoats *(Mustela erminea)* as well as in grey seals *(Halichoerus grypus)* and roe deer *(Capreolus capreolus)*. Implantation is triggered by changes in day length and temperature. Although the mechanism of delayed implantation is understood, many questions remain; for example, why does it occur in American river otters and American mink and not in Eurasian otters and European mink *(Mustela lutreola)*?

Gene flow

Analyses of DNA markers in otter populations on mainland Scotland and the Scottish Islands showed that the further they are apart geographically, the greater the differences in their genetic composition. Shetland otters, for example, because of their distance from the mainland are genetically distinct and have a very low level of genetic diversity. Nonetheless there is no evidence that this lack of genetic diversity has led to an overall reduction in the fitness of the population. The Welsh population, and that in the south west of England, were relatively unaffected by the population crashes of the 1950-1970s. However, both show lower levels of genetic diversity than populations in mainland Scotland, and each has a unique genetic profile. Dallas and colleagues attribute this reduced genetic diversity to the fact that these populations have always been smaller than those in Scotland. Additionally there appears to be little genetic evidence for contact between otters from Wales and from the south west of England. Genetic studies on a regional basis throughout the rest of England have also shown little genetic exchange between populations more than 100km apart and, compared with mainland Scotland, relatively low genetic diversity levels within populations.

Some populations, such as the one in Shetland, are not only genetically distinct but even morphologically distinct. Indeed most otters in Shetland and Ireland actually look different with large varied throat patches.

Mortality and survival

An understanding of the principal causes of otter deaths is necessary before meaningful conservation policies can be formulated. Unfortunately it is very difficult to obtain reliable data from a region because large samples suitable for post-mortem examination are rarely available.

To date the most comprehensive study into otter mortality and survival involved 113 otter carcasses collected throughout Shetland. Deaths were classified as natural (animals that had died from natural causes) and violent (resulting from road traffic or drowning in lobster pots). It was found that approximately 50% of the deaths were in each class over the whole year. However, as illustrated here, while violent deaths happened throughout the year a very high proportion of the non-violent deaths was concentrated in spring. These animals were in poorer condition than those that had died violently, and the mortalities coincided with the period of major food shortage. Seasonal mortality correlated

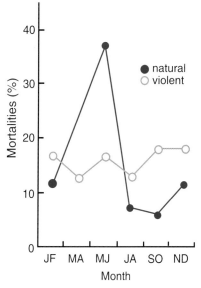

Monthly variation in the mortalities of Shetland otters. Source: Kruuk, Conroy & Moorhouse 1987.

with low numbers of eelpout, rocklings and butter-fish. At this time of the year otters had low hunting success and a majority of the dead animals had died of starvation. Shortage of food in April was also found to be responsible for 40% of the deaths of freshwater otters in northeast Scotland.

Mercury, which occurs naturally in the sea (especially in Shetland), may be a contributory mortality factor since it accumulates in individuals with age. Otters do not have the detoxification mechanism for methyl mercury, which is found in some other marine mammals. Several otters aged five years or more had mercury concentrations considered by some to be lethal. Adult mortality increases significantly with age and average female mortality in Shetland is 31.1% per annum.

The number of otters killed on roads is very high: on Shetland 42% of all otters found dead (which is a biased sample) and 60% of all recorded violent deaths in the United Kingdom were road casualties. About 56% were males but there were definite seasonal peaks with casualties in November and March being five times higher than in June. Interestingly, detailed post mortem analysis carried out by the Veterinary Research Unit in Truro, Cornwall, on 77 otters found dead in south west England showed that a fairly high proportion of all the otters had severe bite wounds, mostly to the face, and genitalia, which had been caused by other otters. There was also evidence of male infanticide. Drowning in lobster pots and fyke nets set for eels are other serious threats. However, it must be borne in mind that the bodies of animals killed on the road are more likely to be found so that the numbers in this compared to other categories may well be exaggerated in samples of otters meeting violent deaths. Nonetheless most causes of violent mortality are thought unlikely to have any serious effect on otter numbers unless populations are fragmented and/or small. Wherever there has been intensive pressure on otters resulting in short term reduction in population size, numbers have usually recovered.

Although otters have a potential lifespan of about 15 years, few ever reach it. On Shetland 19.5% of all dead animals were less than one year old and the mean life expectancy was 3.1 years.

Many of the Shetland otters which died naturally showed evidence of stress. Lack of food at certain times of the year was critical to them and any increase in mercury levels could be disastrous. As a result even a successful population such as that on Shetland is precariously balanced in that any additional pressures could seriously affect its long term viability.

Otter hunting

Otter hunting with hounds dates back to at least the reign of King Henry II who appointed a "King's Otter Hunter" in 1175. This ranks it as the oldest organised form of hunting with hounds in the United Kingdom. For over 500 years it was much more "the sport of kings" than fox hunting ever was. Initially otters were hunted for their skins, then to protect fish stocks and finally for sport.

Otter hunting is thought to have become fashionable in the Elizabethan era, but it was not until the 18th century that it became a sport in its own right. Although otters were still largely regarded as pests until the middle of the 20th century, the hunts also had an interest in ensuring that otters did not become too scarce and ruin the "sport".

In the period 1950-1955, 13 British packs killed 1212 otters averaging between 1.3 and 4.8 days hunting per otter killed. Nevertheless the otter population was able to sustain these losses. The intensity of hunting dropped in the 1960s and 1970s, and by 1976 only nine packs survived. In 1976 these packs found 86 otters but killed only five. The change in the fortunes of the otter hunts came about not as a result of hunting but because the otter population declined for other reasons.

Decline of the otter

It was, not surprisingly, the otter hunters who first noticed that otters appeared to be on the decline. The Wye Valley Otter Hounds were so concerned at the number of blank days they were experiencing that they stopped hunting as early as 1957. By the late 1960s some hunts were calling off hounds once they had picked up an otter's scent and headed them off in another direction in the hope of finding a mink as an alternative quarry. Fortunately, many of the packs kept meticulous hunting records and when these were analysed it was found that hunting success, measured by the number of finds per hundred days hunting, dropped dramatically in 1957/1958, and most severely in the south and east of England.

Otter hunting dwindled and ceased in England and Wales in 1978 when the otter was granted legal protection. This meant that alternative methods were needed to assess the status of the otter population. Accordingly, national surveys were initiated which involved searching for signs of otters on 600 m lengths of river bank every 5-8km along the river. All of Scotland and Wales was searched in this way; in England the country was divided up into 50 km squares using the National Grid and alternate squares were surveyed. The first English survey (1977–78) confirmed that otter numbers had seriously declined; only 6% of the 2940 survey sites were positive. Wales was not much better with 20% of sites positive but Scotland and Ireland had much healthier otter populations with 73% and 91% positive sites respectively. Furthermore, it was found that otters were becoming rare in the Netherlands, western Germany, France and Switzerland.

Hunting success (measured as finds per hundred days) for the Hawkstone, Eastern and Dartmoor Otter Hounds 1950 - 1971. Source: Chanin, 1993.

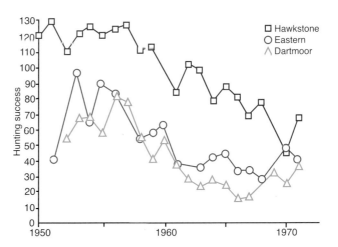

When all the factors, which might have been responsible for the decline, such as habitat destruction, disturbance, killing to protect fisheries and for pelts, road casualties, accidental deaths in traps, severe weather conditions, diseases and pollution, were analysed, the one thought to be the most critical was the introduction of organochlorine pesticides.

Dieldrin, aldrin (chlorinated cyclodienes) and heptachlor were introduced in the 1950s and used extensively as cereal seed dressings and in sheep dips. Raptor populations, particularly the peregrine falcon and the sparrowhawk, were affected dramatically at this time and the cause of the fatalities was traced to the accumulation of these insecticides in the birds' body tissues. Because predators are the top trophic level, they ingest and concentrate significant amounts of the residues, which contaminate their prey. It was inevitable that these insecticides would get into the rivers, leaching through the soil as run-off from fields or as sheep dip effluent. Otters could, therefore, have been particularly vulnerable because they too are top predators. By eating contaminated fish, toxins have accumulated to lethal levels. It is also known that doses of pesticides that are too low to kill an animal can still affect physiological processes, especially reproduction. Sub-lethal effects would have taken much longer to become apparent and animals may well have been sterile for the last years of their lives.

While this largely circumstantial evidence may explain the observed decline in the south and east of England, it appears not to be applicable everywhere. In North Yorkshire, for example, where dieldrin and aldrin were used less extensively and hunting had stopped by 1965, the drop in the otter population occurred much later. Recent information suggests that shooting and trapping during the 1960s may have had a more pronounced effect than is widely thought.

Once the serious effects of dieldrin and aldrin had been recognised these chemicals were withdrawn from general use. The raptors subsequently made a complete recovery and, although the latest national otter surveys are much more encouraging (Wales 53% positive sites, Scotland 87% and England 36%), the otter is still struggling in some regions of the UK and Europe. Why this should be so is not easily explained. It is possible that otter numbers were reduced to such low levels by habitat loss as a result of intensive farming, disturbance, trapping and pollution that populations became physically and socially fragmented, but this is pure speculation.

More recently, there has been concern that polychlorinated biphenyls (PCBs) are seriously affecting otter populations. Like the other organochlorine hydrocarbons they too accumulate in the fatty tissue of mammalian predators. These compounds have been found in otter tissues and spraints at concentrations which give cause for concern but evidence that they have an effect on the otter population is, like that of the other organochlorine compounds, largely circumstantial. Much of the argument is based on experiments carried out on captive mink where it was found that relatively low levels of PCBs seriously impaired reproduction. However, mink are considered to be particularly sensitive to PCBs and the level of tolerance in otters could be much higher. It would appear that more studies are needed on PCB levels and their effect on mink reproduction in the wild. In the light of the Scottish studies it is possible that the effect of toxic chemicals and heavy metals is accentuated in animals already in poor condition as a result of starvation at certain times of the year.

Conservation

Effective conservation requires detailed understanding of the species' ecology. The decline of the Eurasian otter took everyone by surprise and it soon became apparent how little was known about this elusive mammal when that knowledge was most needed. Nonetheless, despite the lack of perfect knowledge, positive action was taken to stop the decline. Otters are protected in England, Wales and Scotland under schedules 5 and 6 of the Wildlife and Countryside Act 1981, making it an offence to kill or trap them or to disturb their breeding areas. Legal protection has been extended throughout Europe under the Bern Convention and the otter is also classified as a species requiring special protection under the EU Habitats Directive (43/93/EEC).

In 1975 the Vincent Wildlife Trust, working closely with landowners and water resource managers, encouraged the protection of riparian habitat. Rivers, where otter still occurred, were identified and havens were established to restore and improve bankside cover and reduce the impacts of human disturbance. This work has now been taken over and expanded by the County Wildlife Trusts and Water UK with the launch of *The Water for Wildlife Project* which works closely with the Environment Agency in implementing the Otter Biodiversity Action Plan. The project now has a workforce of 20 officers and more than 500 volunteers who are involved in river habitat restoration through agri-environmental schemes as well as working closely with other river users. Together with the Environment Agency, guidelines have also been produced for owners of still-water fisheries on how to protect their stocks from otter predation, but at the same time protecting the increasing, but still vulnerable, otter population.

Otter distribution map of the British Isles.
Source: Strachan & Jefferies 1996.

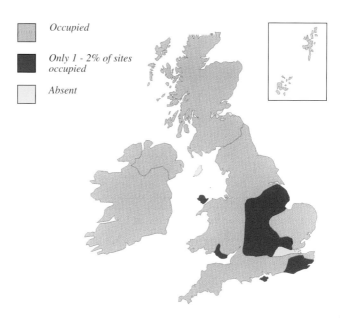

Occupied

Only 1 - 2% of sites occupied

Absent

23

Local Environment Agency Plans, covering England and Wales, and Local Biodiversity Action Plans, covering the whole of the UK, both incorporate actions for otters where relevant.

It is encouraging that the recovery of the English otter population suggested by the 1984 national survey continues as shown by the 1991-1994 and 2000-2002 surveys. Recovery has also been confirmed in separate surveys of Wales (2002) and Scotland (1997). Every one of the 12 regions and catchments into which England was divided for the England survey, shows an increase in the number of positive sites. Recovery has been a result of an expansion from southwest English populations and those on the Welsh borders towards the east, and from northern populations towards the south. Otter reinforcement programmes are also thought to have helped the recovery. Since 1983 55 captive-bred otters from The Otter Trust were released in East Anglia, central and southern England. Between 1990-1993 25 rehabilitated otters from The Vincent Wildlife Trust were released in North Yorkshire and monitored for eight years. A considerable area in North Yorkshire and East Anglia, from which otters were considered absent, is now occupied by these animals and their descendants. It is thought that had these measures not been undertaken the East Anglian population, at least, would undoubtedly have been extinct by 1986.

While the otter is making a comeback, it has taken much longer to return than many other species which disappeared because of pollution. However, following the detailed research carried out by the Institute of Terrestrial Ecology, Banchory on coastal and mainland otters in northeast Scotland, a lot more is known about the otter's sensitivity to prey populations, their need for freshwater pools along coasts, and their use of habitat along streams. It is important to build on this knowledge and now target research into freshwater otter populations in England. There is sometimes a tendency to focus solely on the species rather than, for example, the fish they may eat. Good, healthy, fish populations are vital, and they have to be the right species such as salmonids and eels. For example, otter numbers in some parts of Scotland (Shetland and some lochs in north east Scotland) are declining, perhaps as a consequence of changing fish populations. There has also been an overall decline of eelpout in the North sea and Baltic, due to climate warning and, as discussed (under *Diet*), eelpout were the drivers of otter populations in Shetland. More research is certainly needed on fish populations and their impact on otter recovery. If a catchment is to be managed for otters, we must ensure that there are sufficient populations of prey species. A clearer understanding of sprainting is needed. Unfortunately, assessments of habitat preferences of otters have often been based on spraint distribution, but it has been shown that this may lead to the wrong conclusions. Although spraints are the best and most commonly used evidence that otters are utilising an area, their absence does not mean that otters are not present. Thus the number of spraints may bear little relationship to the density of otters.

Research findings on habitat usage by otters are particularly relevant to otter conservation. Trees along river banks seem to have little effect on otter dispersal or movements. Islands in rivers and lakes, on the other hand, have been shown to attract otters from quite long distances and may be very important habitat features. Thick bushes, bramble, gorse and, in Scotland, rhododendrons are often favoured as lying-up places. Consequently such habitat components may attract otters far more than carefully designed 'artificial holts'. As discussed earlier many otters sleep above ground.

Otters may not be as abundant as they were 40-50 years ago but their future now looks much brighter. However, there is no room for complacency. The current balance between recruitment and survival appears to be very fine and any factor which is likely to affect these processes must be perceived as a serious threat. In conclusion, as Hans Kruuk points out in *Wild otters: Predation and populations*, "The general message for otter conservation, which should come through loud and clear, is that to maintain populations animals will have to be protected as part of an ecosystem, as part of a food web: we have to think in terms of whole wetlands and river catchments." And in *Otters: ecology, behaviour and conservation*. "We need to know more about how nutrients from agriculture and forestry affect fish populations, and how organochlorine compounds, mercury and other pollutants affect their food chain. It is to be hoped that at least some conservation agencies will direct funding towards these ends because national management of wetlands is vitally important."

Acknowledgements

In revising this booklet I have again drawn extensively from recent published research by Professor Hans Kruuk and his colleagues at the Institute of Terrestrial Ecology; also the early radio-tracking work of Jim and Rosie Green at The Vincent Wildlife Trust. If there seems to be an undue emphasis on the ecology of Scottish otters this is because most of the fundamental work has been carried out in Scotland compared with England where otters are very much scarcer. I would, particularly like to thank Professor Hans Kruuk, Dr Geoff Oxford, Dr Andrew Kitchener, Dr Phil Wheeler and Dr Rob Strachan for their helpful advice and comments.

Further reading & sources of information

Further information may be obtained from the following publications:

Carss, D.N. Kruuk, H. and Conroy, J.W.H. (1990) Predation on adult Atlantic salmon (*Salmo salar* L.) by otters (*Lutra lutra* L), within the River Dee system, Aberdeenshire, Scotland. *Journal of Fish Biology* **37**, 935-944.

Chanin, P.R.F. (1993) The Otter in Britain 1900-1990. In *Proceedings of The National Otter Conference, Cambridge 1992*. The Mammal Society, London.

Chanin, P.R.F. (1993). *Otters*. Whittet Books, London.

Chapman, P.J. and Chapman, L.L. (1982) *Otter survey of Ireland 1980-81*. The Vincent Wildlife Trust, London.

Corbet, G. B. & Harris, S. (1991) *The handbook of British mammals* (3rd edn) Blackwell, Oxford.

Conroy, J.W.H., Watt, J., Webb, J., and Jones, A. (2005). *A guide to the identification of prey remains in otter spraints*. The Mammal Society, London.

Crawford, A. (2003). *Fourth otter survey of England 2000-2002*. Environment Agency, Bristol.

Dallas, J.F., Marshall, F., Piertney, S.B., Bacon, P.J. and Racey, P.A. (2002). Spatially restricted gene flow and reduced microsatellite polymorphism in the Eurasian otter *Lutra lutra* in Britain. *Conservation Genetics* **3**, 15-29.

Green, J., Green, R. & Jefferies, D. J. (1984) A radio-tracking survey of otters (*Lutra lutra*) in a Perthshire river system. *Lutra* **27**, 85-145.

Green, J. and Green, R. (1987) *Otter survey of Scotland 1984-1985*. The Vincent Wildlife Trust, London.

Jones, T. and Jones, D. (2004). *Otter survey of Wales 2002*. Environment Agency, Bristol.

Kruuk, H. (1992) Scent marking by otters (*Lutra lutra*): signalling the use of resources. *Behavioural Ecology* **3**, 133-140.

Kruuk, H. (1995) *Wild otters: Predation and populations.* Oxford University Press, Oxford.

Kruuk, H. (2006). *Otters, ecology, behaviour and conservation.* Oxford University Press, Oxford.

Kruuk, H., Conroy, J.W.H. & Moorhouse, A. (1987) Seasonal reproduction, mortality and food of otters (*Lutra lutra* L.) in Shetland. *Symposia of the Zoological Society of London* **58**, 263-278.

Mason, C.F. & Macdonald S.M. (1986) *Otters: Ecology and conservation.* Cambridge University Press, Cambridge (out of print).

MacCaskill, B. (1992) *On the swirl of the tide.* Jonathan Cape, London.

Morris, P. A. (1993) *A Red Data Book for British mammals.* The Mammal Society, London (out of print).

Simpson, V. R. (1997) Health status of otters *(Lutra lutra)* in south west England based on post mortem findings. *Veterinary Record* **141**, 191-197.

Simpson, V. R. and Coxon, K. E. (2000) Intraspecific aggression, cannibalism and suspected infanticide in otters. *British Wildlife* **11**, 423-426.

Strachan, R. and Jefferies, D. J. (1996) *Otter survey of England 1991-1994.* Vincent Wildlife Trust, London.

Thom, T. (1990) *The ecology of otters* (Lutra lutra) *on the Wansbeck and Blyth River catchments in Northumberland.* MSc Thesis, University of Durham.

List of Useful Addresses

(from whom further information about British mammals is available).

The Mammal Society, 2B Inworth Street, London SW11 3EP. www.mammal.org.uk

The Vincent Wildlife Trust, 3 & 4 Bronsil Courtyard, Eastnor, Ledbury, Herefordshire HR8 1EP. www.vwt.org.uk

Natural England, Northminster House, Peterborough PE1 1UA. www.naturalengland.org.uk

The Otter Trust, Earsham, Nr. Bungay, Suffolk NR35 2AF. www.ottertrust.org.uk